IAN SERRAILLIER

ROBIN
IN THE GREENWOOD

Ballads of Robin Hood

ILLUSTRATED BY

VICTOR G. AMBRUS

New York
HENRY Z. WALCK, INCORPORATED
1968

To

J O H N

CONTENTS

Among the Lily-Flower

There are many who sing of grass, of grass,
    And many who sing of corn;
But many who sing of Robin Hood
    Know not where he was born.

It was not in the hall, the hall,
    Nor in the painted bower,
But in the greenwood he was born
    Among the lily-flower.

O Willie was large of limb and bone,
    Of noble rank was he;
To harsh Earl Richard he is gone
    To serve him faithfully.

Earl Richard had but one daughter,
    Fair as the celandine.
'I will not rest,' brave Willie swore,
    'Till I have made you mine.'

It fell upon a summer's night,
    When the leaves were fair and green,
That Willie and his lady dear
    Met in the wood unseen.

'O if my father should get word
    Of the love 'twixt you and me,
No food or drink should pass his lip
    Till you hanged from yonder tree.

'Tomorrow come to my bower, Willie,
    Just as the sun goes down,
And catch me in your sturdy arm,
    And let me not fall down.'

O when the sun was down, was down,
    And the light of the moon was low,
From the window of her bower she looked—
    He stood in the court below.

Into his cloak of scarlet red
    She leaped, fearless of harm;
Willie was large of limb and bone
    And caught her in his arm.

He carried her to the good greenwood,
    And before the night was done
Under the fair and shining leaves
    She bore him a bonny son.

'Lullay, lulla, my little child!
    Lullay, the swinging bough!
I'll rock you, and the nightingale
    Shall be your minstrel now.

'What matter you have no painted bower?
    In the greenwood there's no wall
To mask you from a mother's eye
    Or keep her from your call.'

When night was gone and day was come
    And the sun began to peep,
Earl Richard turned in his bed and woke
    Out of his drowsy sleep.

He rose and called for his merry young men,
    By one, by two, and by three:
'O what's befallen my daughter dear?
    She has not come to me.

'I dreamed a dismal dream last night—
    The storm-wind raged and blew,
And my daughter deep in the sea lay drowned.
    God grant it be not true!

3

'But if my daughter is sick or dead
　　Or falsely stolen away,
I make a vow and I'll keep it true,
　　I'll hang you all this day!'

They sought her here, they sought her there,
　　They sought her up and down;
They found her in the good greenwood,
　　Nursing her bonny young son.

He took the bonny boy in his arms
　　And kissed him tenderly.
'I'd see your father hanged,' he cried,
　　'But your mother's dear to me.

'Dear to me is my grandson too,'
　　And he kissed him once, and again:
'Robin Hood in the good greenwood,
　　O that shall be your name.'

There are many who sing of grass, of grass,
　　And many who sing of corn;
But many who sing of Robin Hood
　　Know not where he was born.

It was not in the hall, the hall,
　　Nor in the painted bower,
But in the greenwood he was born
　　Among the lily-flower.

Seven Foot High

1 THE FIGHT ON THE BRIDGE

It happened one late October day,
    When Robin Hood was twenty,
That, spry as the autumn wind, away
    To find adventure went he.

'We've had no sport for fourteen days—
    Through the golden trees I'll go.
Tarry you here, my men, but hurry
    If I my horn do blow.'

He shook hands with his merry men all
    And bade them all good-bye;
He met a stranger at Barnsley brook,
    Large-limbed and seven foot high.

On the long and narrow bridge they met;
    They both refused to give way.
Then Robin gripped his bow and said,
    'I'll show you Nottingham play.'

From his quiver a broad arrow he drew,
    Feathered from goose's wing.
'I'll liquor your hide,' the stranger replied,
    'If you dare to touch the string.'

'You prate like an ass,' said Robin Hood.
    'Were I to bend my bow,
I'd send an arrow straight to your heart
    Before you struck one blow.'

'You talk like a coward,' the stranger said.
    'See, like a coward you stand
With your bow and arrow, while I have only
    A quarterstaff in my hand.'

Robin laid down his bow and chose
    From the wood a sapling of oak;
He hacked it down, and away he ran
    To the stranger and merrily spoke:

'Look at my staff! It's lusty and tough,
    And here on the bridge we'll play.
Whoever shall knock the other one in
    Shall be the winner, I say.'

'With all my heart,' said the stranger. Robin
    Gave him so heavy a bang
That his bones rattled, his shoulders shook,
    And all his carcass rang.

The stranger swallowed his rage and laughed:
    'So feeble a blow I scorn.
Take this!' And his blows fell thick and fast
    As if he were threshing corn.

He raised his quarterstaff on high,
    He cracked brave Robin's crown;
And from every hair of Robin's head
    The blood came trickling down.

Then Robin sprang at him savagely,
    Laid on and did not tire;   .
He made the stranger billow with smoke
    As if he had been on fire.

Red-faced, the stranger began to boil,
    He gave him a damnable look;
With a sideway swing of his quarterstaff
    He tumbled him into the brook.

'Where are you, good fellow?' the stranger laughed,
    Peering over the side.
Robin's head rose out of the water:
    'Floating along with the tide.'

He splashed through the leaf-choked brook to the bank
    And pulled himself out, by a thorn,
Then shook his coat like a dog and blew
    Three blasts on his bugle-horn.

Over the hills the echo flew,
    And far through valley and wood,
Till lo! his bowmen burst through the trees,
    And there at his side they stood.

2 THE CHRISTENING

'Whatever's the matter?' said William Stutely.
    'Master, you're wet to the skin.'
' 'Tis nothing,' said he. 'I fought with this lad—
    He won, and tumbled me in.'

'Then it's *his* turn to be ducked,' they cried.
    'In he goes, with a heave and a throw!'
And they grabbed his arms. Said Robin Hood,
    'He fought me fair. Let him go.

'No one, good friend, shall lay hands on you.
    These bowmen here are mine—
Three score and eight—if you'll join them too,
    That makes three score and nine.

'You shall be clothed in Lincoln green,
    At your belt a quiver you'll wear;
I'll teach you how to handle the bow
    And shoot at the fallow-deer.'

'O here is my hand,' the stranger replied.
    'I'll serve you with all my heart.
My name is John Little, a man of good mettle—
    Master, I'm ready to start.'

'His name must be changed,' said William Stutely.
    'A christening let me advise.
I'll be his godfather, and here in the wood
    The pretty babe we'll baptize.

'This infant was called John Little,' he said.
    'John Little has fled, he is gone.
The words we'll transpose, and wherever he goes
    He shall be called Little John.'

They cheered as Robin picked up the sweet babe
    And clothed him from top to toe
In garments of gayest Lincoln green,
    And gave him a huge long-bow.

'You'll be the bravest of archers, wed
    To the wood, for better or worse;
But we shall have gold and silver in plenty,
    While bishops have pence in their purse.

'Under the oak, our trysting tree,
    That spans the forest floor,
Where its leafy rafters roof the glade
    A hundred yards and more,

'We live like squires, like lords of the earth,
    Though we own not a foot of free land;
We feast on red deer, with wine and beer,
    And everything at our command.

'But the golden leaves are falling. Soon
    Comes winter—you'll shiver in bed,
While under the freezing stars the icicles
    Drip on your sleeping head.

'Then stout must be your heart and true,
    And blithe must be your song,
For winter stays unbidden, and branches
    Weep the winter long.

'Yet, in coldest February
    The pussy-willow's brave;
It lights the wood and does more good
    Than priests our souls to save.

'For priests live in monstrous pride, unmoved
    If innocent blood is spilled.
But the poor and oppressed we never forget;
    For the old, shelter we build.

'We never lay hands on the labourer,
    Who toils with wagon and plough;
For without his labour how should we live?
    Truly, I know not how.

'The weak, the widow and fatherless,
    The wronged and helpless maid,
With all our power we guard and protect
    And give them bounteous aid.'

With music and dance they finished the day.
    When the sun was low in the west,
And the fox in his den and the birds abed,
    They went to their caves to rest.

The Gallows in the Glen

1 THE BONNY BEGGAR

As Robin Hood rode to Nottingham town
    In his mantle of Lincoln green,
He was aware of a bonny beggar
    Strolling beside a stream.

His hood was ragged, his boots were ripped,
    His coat was patched and torn;
But many a bag hung from his belt—
    These Robin did not scorn.

'God bless you, sir,' said Robin Hood.
    'Where are you from?' said he.
'From Yorkshire, sir; but before you pass,
    Give some money to me.'

'And now I will a-begging go—
    It's time I made a start.' . . .
If you want to know what happened next,
    You must hear the second part.

2 THE WIDOW'S SONS

So Robin walked to Nottingham town,
    With a string of bags to his knee.
His coat and staff weren't worth a penny,
    Yet jauntily went he.

As he skipped along the cobbled streets,
    He heard a pitiful cry,
A widow weeping, 'My three dear sons
    Today are condemned to die.'

'O have they parishes burnt?' said Robin,
    'Or have they ministers slain?
Or have they robbed some innocent maid,
    Or with other men's wives have lain?'

'They have no parishes burnt, good sir,
    Nor yet have ministers slain,
Nor have they robbed some innocent maid,
    Or with other men's wives have lain.'

Then Robin made haste to the sheriff to ask
    If he their lives would spare;
And he skipped and leapt along the streets
    And capered high in the air.

O tough was the sheriff of Nottingham,
    As tough as a carter's horse;
And prickly was his temper too,
    Like furze or moorland gorse.

14

The sheriff it was that answered his knock,
    Arrayed all rich and fine.
'What do you want, you scurvy beggar?
    Speak up. Don't waste my time.'

'No meat or drink,' said Robin Hood,
    'Nor yet to greet your wife.
Three brothers today are condemned to die—
    Pray, spare each brother's life!'

'That cannot be, you cheeky beggar.
    Their guilt is plain and clear.
They're to be hanged in the glen today
    For stealing the King's red deer.'

When they came to the glen, there was many a sob
    And many a weeping eye.
'O hold your peace,' said Robin Hood.
    'I'll see they do not die.'

15

He blew his horn. The pigeons rose
    Wing-clapping from the corn,
And a hundred and fifty bowmen brave
    Stood on the hangman's lawn.

'Master, what is your will?' they said.
    'We will do whatever you wish.'
'Shoot to the east, shoot to the west,
    And see you do not miss.'

They shot to the east, they shot to the west;
    Their arrows were so keen,
Of the gallant sheriff of Nottingham
    Not a sign there was to be seen.

And some of his men had fled, and some
    Lay strewn like leaves on the ground.
Then Robin stepped up to the widow's sons
    And had them each unbound.

And away he went to the good greenwood
    With his hundred and fifty-three—
For the widow's sons went with him too
    And joined his yeomanry.

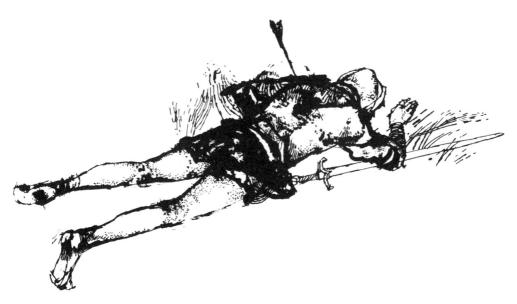

The Strapping Friar of Fountains Dale

How many moons are in the year?
There are thirteen, I say.
But the merriest moon is the midsummer,
Next to the month of May,
When Robin Hood and his merry men
In the greenwood loved to play.

Then some would leap and some would run
And some would shoot with the bow.
'Who can kill a buck?' said Robin,
'And who can kill a doe?
And who can kill a good fat hart
Far off in the glade below?'

Will Scarlet took aim and killed a buck,
And Much he killed a doe,
And Little John killed a good fat hart
Far off in the glade below.

'God bless you, Little John,' said Robin.
　'Your arrow's a joy to watch.
I would ride my horse a hundred miles
　If I could find your match.'

Will Scarlet began to shake with mirth,
　He laughed and said with an oath,
'By the mass, there's a friar at Fountains Abbey,
　And he could beat you both.'

Then Robin swore most solemnly
　By Mary's heavenly grace,
He would not eat or drink till he'd met
　That friar face to face.

He put on his gloves and coat of mail,
　On his head a cap of steel;
With sword and shield and trusty bow
　He rode to Fountains Dale.

When he came to the ford in Fountains Dale,
　No further could he ride;
For he was aware of a strapping friar
　With a giant sword at his side.

Robin Hood leapt down from his horse
　And tethered him. 'Friar,' he said,
'Carry me over the water at once,
　Or I shall shoot you dead.'

The friar took Robin Hood on his back,
　Through the water, stride by stride,
And spoke not a word, good or bad,
　Till he came to the other side.

18

Robin leapt lightly on to the bank.
    Said the friar, when he'd put him down,
'Carry me over the water, fellow,
    Or I shall crack your crown.'

Robin Hood took the friar on his back,
    Through the water, stride by stride,
And spoke not a word, good or bad,
    Till he came to the other side.

The friar leapt lightly on to the bank.
    Then Robin Hood cried again,
'Carry me over the water, friar,
    Or you shall be racked with pain.'

19

The friar took Robin Hood on his back;
   In the middle he tossed him in.
'Choose for yourself, fine fellow,' he cried,
   'Whether you sink or swim.'

Robin swam to a bush of broom,
   The friar to a willow wand;
Robin hauled himself to the bank
   And took his bow in his hand.

He drew his best arrow from under his belt
   And swiftly let it fly;
But the friar warded it off with his shield
   And turned it glancing by.

'Shoot on,' said the friar, 'fine fellow, shoot on,
   For you've hardly yet begun.'
Robin Hood shot passing well,
   Till all his arrows were gone.

So they took their swords and fought from ten
   Till four in the afternoon.
Then Robin Hood dropped to his knees
   To beg from the friar a boon.

'A boon, a boon, you strapping friar!
   I beg you on my knee
To let me set my horn to my mouth
   And blow blasts two and three.'

'I grant it gladly,' the friar replied.
   'You have plenty of wind, no doubt.
I hope you'll blow so passing well
   That both your eyes fall out.'

Robin Hood set his horn to his mouth,
   He blew both loud and shrill;
And half a hundred yeomen brave
   Came hastening over the hill.

'Whose men are these?' exclaimed the friar,
    'That race the woodland through?'
'These men are mine,' said Robin Hood,
    'But what is that to you?'

'A boon, a boon I beg,' said the friar,
    'For a boon you begged from me.
Let me set my fist to my mouth
    And whistle whistles three.'

'I grant it gladly,' Robin replied,
    'You can blow till your hair is grey.
Three whistles in a friar's fist—
    May they blast your teeth away!'

The friar set his fist to his mouth,
    He whistled whistles three;
And half a hundred savage dogs
    Came leaping over the lea.

Two together at Robin leapt,
    A golden and a black;
Robin's mantle of Lincoln green
    They ripped from off his back.

But whether his men shot arrows east
    Or west or north or south,
Those dogs, so smartly trained they were,
    Each caught them in his mouth.

'Call off your dogs,' said Little John.
    'Friar, do as you're told.'
'Whose man are you,' the friar said,
    'To speak so brash and bold?'

'I am Little John, Robin Hood's man,
    And, friar, I tell you true,
If you do not call off your dogs at once,
    I'll shoot both them and you.'

Little John took his brave long-bow;
    He drew it again and again.
Soon half a score of the friar's dogs
    Lay dead on the grassy plain.

'Enough, good fellow,' the friar he cried,
    'Let your master and me be friends.
He shall command—I, Friar Tuck,
    Will take what Heaven sends.'

'If you will leave fair Fountains Dale,'
    Said Robin, 'and quit the ford,
Every Sunday throughout the year
    Ten shillings shall be your reward.

'Each holy day throughout the year
    New garments you shall wear,
If you will go to merry Sherwood
    And tarry with me there.'

'Seven years I've lived in Fountains Dale
    And kept the Abbey door;
And neither knight nor lord nor earl
    Could make me leave before.
But from today I'm Robin's man,
    And will serve him evermore.'

How many moons are in the year?
    There are thirteen, I say.
But the merriest moon is the midsummer,
    Next to the month of May,
When Robin Hood and his merry men
    In the greenwood loved to play.

The Bishop who Danced in his Boots

Come, gentlemen all, and listen awhile,
    And a story I will unfold,
How Robin treated the Bishop to dinner
    And robbed him of all his gold.

It happened in merry Barnsley Dale,
    Under the greenwood tree,
The Bishop of Hereford was due to come by
    With all his company.

'Come, kill me a deer,' said bold Robin Hood,
    'A good fat deer to eat.
The Bishop is dining with me today,
    And he shall pay well for the treat.

'We'll kill a fat deer to roast at the fire
    And dress by the highway-side,
And we'll watch for the Bishop warily,
    Lest some other way he should ride.'

23

He clothed himself and six of his men
   With crooks, in shepherds' attire,
And when the Bishop came prancing by,
   They were roasting the deer at the fire.

'Whatever is this?' the Bishop he asked.
   'For whom is this sumptuous spread?
And why have you killed the King's fat deer
   When there are so few to be fed?'

'We are humble shepherds,' said bold Robin Hood,
   'Who tend our sheep all the year;
And as we're disposed to be merry today,
   We have killed the King's fat deer.'

'Impertinent fellows!' the Bishop exclaimed.
   'The King of your doings shall know.
Therefore make haste and come with me—
   For straight to the King you shall go.'

'O pardon, O pardon,' said bold Robin Hood,
   'O pardon, good Bishop, I pray!
It is hardly right for a lord of the church
   To take our lives away.'

'No pardon, no pardon,' the Bishop replied.
   'I tell you my answer is no.
Therefore make haste and come with me—
   For straight to the King you shall go.'

Robin Hood set his back to a tree
   And his foot to the root of a thorn,
Then from under the flap of his shepherd's coat
   He pulled out a bugle-horn.

He put the little end to his mouth
   And blew a loud blast, and lo!
Three score and ten of Robin Hood's men
   Were standing there in a row.

24

Deep they bowed to their master dear—
    'Twas a splendid sight to see.
'What is the matter?' said Little John.
    'You blow so hastily.'

'O here is the Bishop of Hereford, John.
    Our lives he refuses to save.'
'Cut off his head, master,' said John,
    'And throw him into his grave.'

'O pardon, O pardon,' the Bishop cried out.
    'O pardon, Robin, I pray!
For if I had known I'd meet with you,
    I'd have gone some other way.'

'No pardon, no pardon,' Robin replied.
    'I tell you my answer is no.
Therefore make haste and come with me—
    For to Barnsley Dale you shall go.'

25

Then Robin Hood took His Grace by the hand
    And led him to Barnsley Dale;
He made him stay to dinner and drink
    Good wine and beer and ale.

'Bring me the bill,' said the Bishop. 'It must
    Be mounting monstrous high.'
'Lend me your purse,' said Little John,
    'And I'll settle it by and by.'

Then Little John took the Bishop's cloak
    And spread it wide on the ground,
And out of the Bishop's bulging purse
    He poured three hundred pound.

'Here's money enough, master,' said John.
    ' 'Tis a splendid sight to see.
I'd like to give the dear Bishop a kiss,
    Though he cannot care much for me.'

'He shall sing us a mass ere he goes,' said Robin,
    Then bound him fast to a tree
And made him sing mass from beginning to end
    To all his yeomanry.

Then Robin Hood led him away through the wood
    And called for music to play,
And he made the Bishop dance in his boots;
    Then, astride his dapple-grey,
He gave the Bishop the tail in his hand—
    He was glad to gallop away!

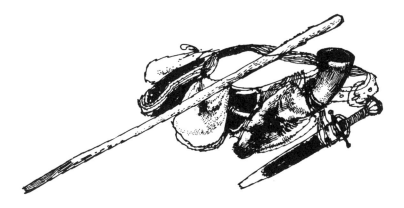

A Dream of Two Yeomen

1 ROBIN HOOD'S DREAM

Bright with dew were the grassy banks
    When the sun began to peep;
The owl was driven to bed, but the greenfinch
    Roused himself from sleep.

O loud and lustily he sang
    To greet the glad new day;
So loud his note brave Robin he woke
    In the greenwood where he lay.

'Now by my faith,' said Robin, 'strange
    Was the dream I had last night;
I dreamed, two sturdy yeomen bold
    Fast with me did fight.

'They beat and bound me and took my bow,
    They gave my crown a crack.
If there be any truth in this,
    I swear I'll pay them back.'

27

'Master, dreams are swift,' said John,
  'As the wind that blows on the hill;
No matter how loud and rough tonight,
  Tomorrow it may be still.'

'I wonder, who were these men?' said Robin.
  'The sheriff was one, 'twould seem.
With seven score men he seeks us out—
  But who else was in my dream?

'Make ready, make ready, my merry men all,
  And John shall go with me,
For I'm going to search the woods for them
  And find who they may be.'

2 THE MAN IN THE HORSE'S HIDE

They put on their gowns of Lincoln green,
  They took their bows of yew,
And away through the leafy glades they went
  To search the forest through.

But when they came to the merry greenwood,
  Where most they loved to be,
They were aware of a sturdy yeoman
  Leaning against a tree.

He wore at his side a dagger and sword,
  (Which deal in death and pain),
And he was clad in a horse's hide,
  Top and tail and mane.

'Stand still, master,' said Little John,
  'Under this tree so green,
And I will go up to that sturdy yeoman
  To know what he can mean.'

'Ah, John! You understand me not,
    And that most strange I find.
When do I send my men in front
    And tarry myself behind?

'You can tell a man from his speech,—and that's
    No trick,' his master said.
'Were it not that I prize my bow,
    I'd break it over your head.'

As an angry word distress can bring,
    They parted, Robin and John;
And John he went to Barnsley Dale—
    He knew the paths, each one.

But when he came to Barnsley Dale,
    Heavy the tears he shed;
For two of his fellows in Lincoln green
    Lay in the bracken, dead.

And fleet of foot Scarlet was flying
    Fast over stump and stone,
But hot at his heels and faster followed
    The sheriff and seven score men.

Then John did bend his brave long-bow,
    He drew the string to shoot;
But the bow was made from a tender bough
    And down it fell at his foot.

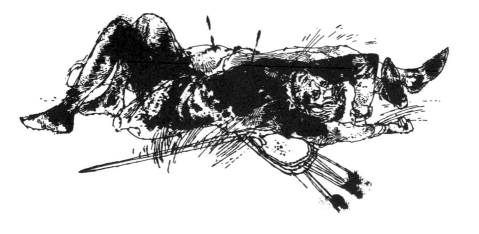

'O wicked wood, most wicked wood
    That ever grew on a tree!
Distress and grief to me you bring—
    You should my comfort be.'

His arrow was but loosely shot,
    Yet did not fly in vain,
For one of the sheriff's men it struck—
    And William a Trent was slain.

When men do meet, as the saying goes,
    Five can do more than three;
So the sheriff lay hold of Little John
    And bound him fast to a tree.

'You shall be dragged by dale and down
    And hanged high on a hill!'
'That cannot be,' said Little John,
    Unless it is God's will.'

Let us leave Little John bound to the tree
    And talk of Robin Hood.
He stepped right up to that sturdy yeoman,
    Where under the leaves he stood.

'Good morrow, good fellow,' said bold Robin Hood.
    'Good morrow, good fellow,' said he.
'I think from the bow you hold in your hand,
    A good archer you must be.'

'Wild are these woodland ways—I'm lost,'
    The sturdy yeoman replied.
'I'll lead you through the wood,' said Robin.
    'Good fellow, I'll be your guide.'

'I seek an outlaw,' the stranger said.
    'Men call him Robin Hood.
I long to find him—forty guineas
    I'd count not half so good.'

'Come with me now, you sturdy yeoman,
    And Robin you soon shall see;
But first, sir, let us enjoy some sport
    Under the greenwood tree.

' 'Tis fit some trial of skill we have,
    To practise let us prepare,
Lest we chance to meet with Robin Hood
    And he catch us unaware.'

A willow wand they set in the ground
    Three hundred yards away.
'Lead on,' said Robin. 'No, *you*,' said the yeoman,
    'Shall be the first to play.'

The first arrow brave Robin did shoot,
    By an inch he missed the wand;
The yeoman he was an archer good,
    But his bolt flew far beyond.

The second arrow the yeoman did shoot,
    It grazed the wand as it flew;
But Robin he shot far better again—
    He cleft the wand in two.

'God bless your heart,' the yeoman said.
    'Your shooting is wondrous good;
For if your heart be as true as your hand,
    You are better than Robin Hood.

'Now tell me your name, good fellow,' said he,
    'Under the leaves of lime.'
Said Robin Hood, 'You must tell me yours
    Before I tell you mine.'

'I dwell by dale and down,' said the yeoman.
    'To capture Robin I came.
My home is Fountains Abbey, and Guy
    Of Gisborne is my name.'

'My roof and walls are of oak,' said Robin,
    'My home is Barnsley wood.
I am the man you have sought so long,
    For my name is Robin Hood.'

4 THE BUGLE-HORN

They drew their swords, they clashed together—
    O, 'twas a splendid sight
To see these yeomen strike and thrust
    With blades all burnished bright.

Fiercely, furiously they fought
    Two hours of a summer's day;
Yet neither Sir Guy nor Robin Hood
    Did flinch or fly away.

Then Robin aimed at his heart—and fell,
    On a hawthorn root he tripped.
Sir Guy was nimble and quick, he lunged
    At Robin's side, as he slipped.

'Dear Mary, Mother of God,' cried Robin,
    'O help me now, I pray!
I think it was never man's destiny
    To die before his day.'

Our Lady heard his prayer, and Robin
    At once leaped up again.
A straight back-handed blow he struck—
    Sir Guy on the ground lay slain.

The yeoman's horn he took from his pouch
    And a loud blast he blew.
The sheriff he heard it ring through the wood—
    That bugle note he knew.

'Hark!' cried the sheriff. 'Hark, O hark!
    The news I hear is good.
Sir Guy has blown his bugle-horn—
    He has slain Robin Hood.'

He put his horn to his mouth, and once,
    Then once again he blew,
To tell Sir Guy he had heard his call
    And himself had triumphed too.

At the first note bold Robin was glad,
    At the second he lost his cheer.
'The sheriff has raided Barnsley Dale
    And mischief done, I fear.'

He pulled his Irish knife from his belt
    And slashed Sir Guy in the face,
So never a man of woman born
    That treacherous knight could trace.

'Lie there, lie there, you scurvy knave!
    I hope no grudge you'll bear.
Though worse were the strokes you got from me,
    Yet better the clothes you'll wear.'

He took off his gown of green and threw it
    Over his lifeless foe,
Then dressed himself in the horse's hide—
    It covered him, top to toe.

'Your bow and arrows and bugle-horn
    I'll take, for it's time to be going,
And I must away to Barnsley Dale
    To see how my men are doing.'

The Two Penniless Priests

I have heard tales of Robin Hood
  And valiant Little John,
Of Will Scarlet and Friar Tuck,
  And Much, the miller's son.

But such a tale as this one, how
  As a friar, ragged and poor,
Robin Hood disguised himself,
  I never heard before.

With rosary, gown and crucifix,
  And black and tattered hood,
He said good-bye to his merry men all
  And took the road from the wood.

He had not gone a mile, a mile,
  A mile but barely three,
When he chanced to spy two priests in black
  Come riding gallantly.

'God bless you both,' said Robin Hood.
    'God bless my blistered feet,
For I've been wandering all day long
    Without a crumb to eat,

'Without so much as a drop to drink—
    O pity on me take,
And cross my hand with a silver shilling
    For our dear Lady's sake!'

'Money?' the priests replied. 'By the mass,
    We swear we haven't any.
This very morning we were attacked
    And robbed of every penny.'

'I am much afraid,' said Robin Hood,
    'That you two priests are lying.
Before you go, I'll learn the truth—
    There is no harm in trying.'

The priests turned pale, they fled like the squall
    That drives the winter rain;
But Robin took to his heels and quickly
    Caught them up again.

He grabbed them both and from their horses
    Pulled them to the ground,
'O spare us, friar! In our pockets, look—
    There's nothing to be found.'

'What! Are your pockets empty?' said Robin.
    'You have no money, you say?
Well then, the three of us must kneel
    And for money humbly pray.'

The priests began to sweat for fear,
    They knelt with pretty speed.
'Send us, merciful Lord,' they prayed,
    'Money to meet our need.'

Most mournfully they uttered prayers,
　　Their hands sadly wringing;
They wept and groaned aloud, but Robin
　　Merrily kept singing.

An hour they prayed, and loud and louder
　　Rose the priests' lament.
'Now let's see,' said Robin Hood,
　　'What money Heaven has sent.

' 'Tis fair we share it all, and each
　　His portion shall receive;
But woe betide the man who dares
　　His fellows to deceive.'

The priests dug into their pockets deep,
    But money found they none.
'We'll search each other,' said Robin Hood,
    'Thoroughly, one by one.'

With patient care he searched them both;
    He found a lavish hoard.
Five hundred golden guineas soon
    Upon the grass he poured.

'It does me good,' said Robin Hood,
    'Such store of gold to see;
And both of you deserve your share,
    You prayed so heartily.'

He gave them fifty pounds apiece,
    And the rest for himself did keep.
The priests they dared not speak one word,
    But their sighs were wondrous deep.

Shamefaced they staggered to their feet
    And said, ' 'Tis time to part.'
'Wait,' said Robin, 'I've something more
    To say before you start.

'You both shall swear by all the saints
    Upon this holy grass,
That you will never tell lies again,
    Whichever way you pass.

'The second oath you shall take is this:
    To be generous to the poor . . .
If questioned, say you have met with a friar,
    And I desire no more.'

He set them on their horses again—
    To their priory they spurred;
Then he returned to the good greenwood,
    As sprightly as a bird.

The Cunning Beggar

1 THE CUDGEL-STAFF

One afternoon ere spring had come,
    And wind and rain were blowing,
Robin set out from Barnsley Dale—
    To the greenwood he was going.

He met a beggar along the way;
    Sturdy was the beggar's step,
In his hand a mighty cudgel-staff
    That bristled in his grip.

He wore an old and tattered cloak
    That clung to him, fold on fold;
He'd wrapped it round him twenty times
    To keep him from the cold.

Three battered hats were on his head,
    Rammed down and stuck together;
He minded not the wind and wet,
    He walked in any weather.

A leather bag hung from his neck,
    Tied by a leather string
And clasped across. As he stumped along,
    Gruffly he did sing.

'Tarry, tarry,' good Robin called,
    'Tarry, and speak with me.'
'It's much too late. Why should I wait?'
    He answered peevishly.

'I've far to go to my lodging-house;
    The path is rough and hilly.
If supper's finished when I arrive,
    I shall look wondrous silly.'

'I've eaten nothing,' said Robin. 'Tonight
    I know not where I'll lie.
And should I to the tavern go,
    I have no money to buy.

'Therefore I ask, till next we meet,
    Spare me a penny to spend.'
The beggar answered grumpily,
    'I have no money to lend.'

'Lay down your tattered cloak,' said Robin.
    'Do not so stiffly stand.
Undo the string of your leather bag,
    Or I'll rip it with my hand.

'And I swear by Mary, Mother of God,
    If you make the slightest din,
I'll see if a silver arrow-head
    Can pierce a beggar's skin.'

The beggar smiled. 'Would you frighten me
    With your pack of brittle sticks?
You'd better leave me alone. They're only
    Fit for *pudding-pricks.

'I defy you now to do me harm,
    For all your stormy bluster.
Your arrow or my cudgel-stick—
    We'll see which flies the faster.'

* Wooden skewers for fastening the end of a gut containing a pudding.

45

Good Robin bent his noble bow—
    His cheeks were red with anger—
And in it he set a broad arrow;
    But before he drew his finger,

The beggar's mighty cudgel-staff
    Struck him such a blow
That Robin's arrow snapped in two
    And splintered was his bow.

Good Robin took to his heels and ran—
    Alas, he ran in vain,
For the beggar struck him hard on the hand
    With the cudgel-staff again,

So hard that he could not draw his sword
    For forty days and more.
Good Robin could not speak a word,
    So heavy his heart and sore.

He could not fight, he could not fly,
    He knew not what to do.
The beggar's mighty cudgel-staff
    Beat him black and blue.

He struck poor Robin back and side,
    He chased him up and down;
With his cudgel-staff he clubbed him till
    He fainted on the ground.

'Stand up! Stand up!' the beggar cried.
    ' 'Tis only cowards rest.
Stay and count your money, sir;
    That course would be your best.

'Then after go to the tavern-house
    And buy both wine and ale
For all your friends to drink your health,
    When they hear your pretty tale.'

Good Robin answered never a word;
    Still as a stone he lay;
Closed were both his eyes, his cheeks
    Were white as china clay . . .
The beggar thought that Robin was dead
    And briskly walked away.

2 ROBIN'S PLAN

Will Scarlet, Much, and Little John
    Chanced to walk that way;
They found good Robin motionless
    In the greenwood where he lay.

They picked him up, their master dear—
    O melancholy task!
What fiendish rogue had laid him low?
    There wasn't a soul to ask.

They looked for wounds, but none they found,
    Though they felt him round about;
He rolled and gasped and groaned aloud,
    And the blood came belching out.

They ran for water from the stream
    And splashed it into his face.
He opened his eyes; with a weary sigh
    He told them of his disgrace.

'I have been watchman in this wood
    For nearly forty year,
Yet never was I so hard beset
    As you have found me here.

'A beggar wearing a tattered cloak,
    From whom I feared no ill,
Clawed my back with a cudgel-staff—
    I fear 'twill never get well.

47

'Yonder over the hill he went,
    With three hats stuck on his head;
If ever you loved your master, O
    Go and revenge this deed.'

'I'll stay with you, master,' said Little John,
    'Your dreadful pain to ease.
Let Much and Scarlet bring him back,
    To do with as you please.'

'Take care—if there's room to swing his staff,'
    Said Robin, 'he'll crack your crown.'
'No dirty beggar with a cudgel-staff,'
    Said Much, 'shall knock us down.'

'Then lie in ambush among the trees,
    Leap out before he hits,
And grab the cudgel-staff from his hand,
    Or he'll bang you both to bits.'

Away they went, but John remained.
    He lifted Robin, and smiled:
'I must teach you, master, to walk again,
    For you toddle like a child.'

3 THE LEATHER BAG

Scarlet and Much knew the country well,
    Every curve and quarter;
They guessed the way the beggar had gone;
    Their way was three miles shorter.

Strongly, sturdily they ran,
    They splashed through pool and mire,
By hill and valley, forest and field—
    They did not droop or tire,

Till they saw the beggar pressing behind:
    He passed through a wicket-gate.
A hazel-thicket stood between,
    And there they lay in wait.

And as he scurried past them both,
    They sprang at him, two abreast;
Much grabbed his staff, and Scarlet held
    A dagger to his chest.

Much hurled the cudgel-staff in the air
    And stuck it into the green.
The beggar was loth to see it go,
    He wished it had not been;
He cringed with fear, more terrified
    Than any man they'd seen.

'Have mercy on me!' the beggar whined.
    'And take away that knife!
I never hurt you or anyone,
    I swear, in all my life '

'You lie, you dirty rogue!' they cried.
  'And falsely you have sworn.
You nearly killed the bravest man
  That ever yet was born.

'And now we'll take you back with us
  Fast bound, and then you'll see
Whether you die on our master's sword
  Or dangle from a tree.'

The beggar cried out in black despair;
  His heart was mortal sick;
He glared at them through his lizard eyes
  And yearned for his cudgel-stick.
Then, as a gusty wind blew up,
  He thought of a cunning trick.

'What will you gain by butchering
  A snivelling wretch like me?
A beggar's blood, brave gentlemen,
  Is hardly worth a flea.

' 'Tis true I struck your master down,
  But only in self-defence;
And now, if you'll set me free and promise
  No further violence,
I'll show you my good faith and make you
  Handsome recompense.

'Deep in the folds of this leather bag
  I have hidden a hundred pound.
Let me go, and I'll give it all to you—
  I'll pour it out on the ground.'

Scarlet and Much took counsel, then
  They let the beggar go;
They knew if he took to his heels and ran,
  They'd catch him up below.

'You have done mischief enough,' they said,
    'And now let's see your gold.'
He grinned and took off his tattered cloak—
    It lay on the ground, unrolled.

He lifted the leather bag from his neck—
    There was only flour inside—
And laid it down on the tattered cloak;
    The mouth he opened wide.

He turned, so the wind was behind his back,
    Craftily changing places;
Then he plunged both hands into the flour
    And flung it into their faces.

They coughed and spluttered and closed their eyes—
    For a moment both were blind.
They spread out their arms—where was the rogue?
    In front of them? Behind?

The beggar grabbed for his stick, then jeered,
    'The wind so fiercely blows,
I fear I must use my cudgel-stick
    To beat the flour from your clothes.'

He clobbered them right lustily—
    O pity their wounds and weals!
But when they'd rubbed the flour from their eyes,
    They turned and took to their heels.

'Why this hurry?' the beggar jeered.
    'Have you forgotten your prize,
The hundred pounds I promised? Or is
    There still some flour in your eyes?
My cudgel-staff could clean them out;
    Perhaps that would be wise.'

Scarlet and Much said never a word;
    They could only splutter and blink.
And the beggar vanished over the hill
    Before they had time to think.

4 THE RETURN

Night was falling. To search for him
    Would be hopeless and in vain;
But you can guess how ashamed they looked
    When they came to Robin again.

'How did you fare?' good Robin asked.
    They answered, 'None too well.'
'That cannot be. By the look of your clothes
    You have both been to the mill.
There's plenty of food in the miller's house,
    And you have eaten your fill.'

They hung their heads, they sank to the ground,
    Not a word they dared to speak.
'Because I fainted, do you fancy that you
    Can lie on the ground for a week?'

Then they told him how they had caught the rogue,
    How the flour had made them blind,
And how the beggar's cudgel-staff
    With weals their backs had lined;

And how they could hardly scramble home,
    Their bones were so stiff and sore.
'Fie, for shame!' cried Robin Hood.
    'We're disgraced for evermore.'

And yet, though sad he was unrevenged,
    He could not help but laugh
To think how his merry young men had tasted
    The beggar's cudgel-staff.

The Greedy Butchers

1 THE ROAD TO NOTTINGHAM

Come to me, all you young gallants, O come
    From town and meadow and wood!
If you listen a while, I'll sing you a song
    Of an archer, bold Robin Hood.

Once, as he walked in the merry greenwood,
    It chanced bold Robin did see
A butcher astride a bonny fine mare,
    And riding to market was he.

'Good morrow, good fellow,' said Robin Hood.
    'What carry you there in your pack?
And tell me your trade and where you dwell—
    I trust you'll safely get back.'

The butcher he answered Robin Hood,
    'What matters it where I dwell?
For a butcher am I, and to Nottingham town
    I am going, my meat to sell.'

53

'What is the price of your mare?' said Robin.
  'Tell me, I'm eager to learn.
And what is the price of your meat, for I wish
  As a butcher my living to earn?'

'The price of my meat?' the butcher replied.
  'I can reckon that up in a minute . . .
Four shillings, good sir, is none too dear—
  And a bonny fine mare to go with it.'

'Four guineas I'll give you,' said Robin Hood,
  'Four guineas in gold I'll pay.'
They counted their money, exchanged their clothes,
  And each rode off on his way.

2 THE MARKET

So Robin Hood rode to Nottingham town
  On the butcher's bonny fine mare.
Though others might charge too dear for their meat,
  He vowed *his* price should be fair.

But the sheriff he was in league with these rogues,
  He too was a twister and cheat.
What cared he if the price was too high
  And the poor could buy no meat?

In their stalls the butchers opened their meat,
  On dish and platter displayed;
For many a year they'd swindled the poor,
  But Robin was new to the trade.

Yet not a bite, not a morsel they sold,
  While bountiful Robin did well:
He sold more meat for one penny piece
  Than the rest for three pennies could sell.

Those villainous butchers fell back, amazed;
   The sheriff he scratched his head.
'If this fellow continues in trade, we'll starve.
   We must teach him a lesson,' they said.

The butchers stepped over to Robin, resolved
   That some pretty trick should be played.
'Good brother,' said one, 'will you join us for dinner?
   Do come—we are all in the trade.'

'Such offers,' said Robin, 'I never refuse.'
   And to dinner they hurried apace.
The sheriff sat down at the head of the table,
   And asked Robin Hood to say grace.

'And when you've said grace, you shall sit at my side
   And we'll drink to success and long life.'
'I'll gladly say grace,' said bold Robin Hood,
   'If I may sit next to your wife.'

The sheriff agreed. 'God bless us!' said Robin.
   'Good appetite! Drink your fill!
Though five pounds and more it cost me in gold,
   I vow that I'll settle the bill.'

'This fellow is crazy,' the butchers declared.
   Said the sheriff, 'He's due for a fall.
He has sold all his land for silver and gold,
   And means to squander it all.'

'May he squander it all in this house,' said the
                                             butchers,
   'And part with it, quick as can be!'
'Be patient! I've thought of a trick,' said the sheriff.
   'I beg you to leave it to me.'

3 INTO THE GREENWOOD

Said the sheriff to Robin, 'What have you to sell?
    Any cattle or hornéd beast?'
'Indeed, I have plenty, good master sheriff,
    Two or three hundred at least.'

The sheriff saddled his dapple-grey,
    With three hundred pound in gold;
And away he went with bold Robin Hood,
    His hornéd beasts to behold.

By hill and furrow and field they rode,
    To the forest of merry Sherwood.
'O, Heaven forbid,' the sheriff exclaimed,
    'That we meet with Robin Hood!'

'Why do you tremble and shake?' said Robin.
    'You should trust, good sir, in me.
With my brave long-bow and arrows I'll show
    I can shoot as straight as he.'

When to a leafy hollow they came,
    Bold Robin chanced to spy
A hundred head of good red deer
    Through the trees come tripping by.

'Good master sheriff, how like you my beasts?
    They're sleek—and see how they race!'
'I tell you, good fellow, I'd rather go home—
    I don't like the look on your face.'

Then Robin Hood put his horn to his mouth,
  He blew blasts two and three—
And fifty bowmen with brave Little John
  Stood under the greenwood tree.

'What is your will?' then said Little John.
  'Good master, what must we do?'
'I have brought the sheriff of Nottingham town
  Today to have dinner with you.'

'He is welcome indeed,' said Little John.
  'I hope from his purse he will pay
Guineas and shillings to give to the poor,
  To gladden them many a day.'

Robin Hood stripped the cloak from his back
  And, laying it down on the ground,
He emptied the purse—in silver and gold
  He counted three hundred pound.

Then lo! through the greenwood the sheriff he led,
  Sitting glum on his old dapple-grey.
'Remember me, sir, to your lady at home!'
  Laughed Robin, and galloped away.

The Sheriff's Prisoner

1 THE QUARREL

In summer, when the leaves are large and long
    And thrush and blackbird sing,
How merry under the boughs to walk
    And hear the woodland ring,

To see the deer draw to the dale
    And leave the hills so high
And shadow them to the good greenwood,
    Where under the trees they lie.

It happened at joyous Whitsuntide,
    One early morning in May;
The sun was out, and so were the birds—
    They sang from twig and spray.

Then Robin took a two-handed sword,
    Hanging down at his knee;
He ran outside, and into the crowd
    Like a winged arrow went he.

He wounded many a mother's son,
    And twelve of them he slew;
Then on the sheriff's steel-capped head
    He broke his sword in two.

'O curse the smith that forged this blade!
    I'm weaponless!' Back he plunged
Into the church, and the rabble swept in—
    With stick and stave they lunged.

They struck him down, they carried him high
    In triumph through the street,
Then flung him into the castle jail,
    With fettered wrists and feet.

3 THE ROAD TO LONDON

When Little John heard where Robin lay,
    Heavy the tears he shed.
'O why did I leave my master dear?
    I wish that I were dead.'

'Tomorrow to the King at Westminster,'
    Said Much, 'the monk will ride.
He carries the sheriff's letter.' Said John,
    'This monk must be defied.'

'My uncle lives by the London road,'
    Said Much, 'near the hazel-wood.'

'We'll go there at once,' said John. Next day,
    As they at the window stood,
They saw the monk go riding past—
    They knew him by his hood.

Outside they hailed him courteously.
    'Good abbot, tell us, pray,
Have you heard any news of Robin Hood,
    Who was captured yesterday?

'He robbed us both of twenty pounds—
    Money we ill could spare.'
'He robbed me too,' said the angry monk,
    'A hundred pounds, I swear.

'He hurled me from my horse and left me
    Half dead by a mossy bank . . .
But I was the first to lay hands on him,
    And for that you've me to thank.'

'May God reward you, courageous monk.
    You must be badly shaken.
Can we guide you through the wood? His men
    Will attack when they hear he's taken.'

Much took the horse's bridle, and straight
    Through the wood the way he led.
Then Little John pulled the monk from his horse,
    And cut off his hooded head . . .
And there, in the damp and marshy ground,
    They dug his muddy bed.

4 THE KING AT WESTMINSTER

Away they rode to Westminster;
    John knelt before the King:
'God save you, sir! From Nottingham town
    The sheriff's letter we bring.'

The King broke open the sheriff's seal.
    'What! Robin in jail?' cried he.
'There's never a yeoman in all the land
    I long so much to see.

'Where is the monk who carried this letter?
    He should be here today.'
'Alas, Your Grace,' said Little John,
    'He fell ill and died on the way.'

Then the King made Much and Little John
    Yeomen of the Crown;
He gave them twenty pounds and a letter
    For the sheriff of Nottingham town:
'Bring Robin Hood to Westminster,
    And deliver him safe and sound.'

Back they spurred to Nottingham. 'Porter,
    Why have you locked the gate?
We've ridden post haste from London town,
    We're carrying Letters of State.'

'Robin Hood's in jail,' said the porter.
    'Our garrison mans the walls.
With every arrow his bowmen shoot,
    One of our soldiers falls.

'Will Scarlet, Stutely, and all his band
    Plague us day after day;
But since you come from the King, good yeoman,
    I'll open the gate straightway.'

5 THE ESCAPE

With clattering hoof to the sheriff's house
    They spurred. He bared his head,
As he tore apart the royal seal,
    And the King's letter he read.
'Where is the monk who carried my letter?
    Is he here?' the sheriff said.

64

'The King took such a fancy to him,'
    Said John, 'I'm told to say
He made him Abbot of Westminster,
    And that's where he is today.'

'Bravo, good yeoman,' the sheriff said.
    'Now drink! Here's wine of the best.'
Then the sheriff and Much and Little John
    Went up to bed to rest.

The sheriff lay snoring wheezily,
    Sodden with wine and ale.
Little John and Much crept out of bed
    And ran to the castle jail.

They drummed on the jailer's door. 'Rise up!
    Sluggard, get out of bed!
The traitor Robin Hood has escaped!
    Your prisoner has fled!'

The jailer bundled out of his bed,
    The moment he heard them call.
Then Little John drew out his sword
    And stood him against the wall.

'My turn to be porter—give me your keys,'
    Said John. 'You cannot resist.'
He unlocked Robin's dungeon door,
    Unfettered him, foot and wrist.

He gave him a nut-brown sword in his hand,
    Which steadfastly he gripped;
From the lowest side of the castle wall
    Down like deer they leapt.

At dawn, when the cock stood up to crow
    And day began to spring,
The sheriff he found the jailer slain.
    'O ring the bell, O ring!

'Let the crier shout through Nottingham streets,
    "If Robin Hood be found,
The man who brings him to me alive
    Shall earn a hundred pound."

'Alone,' said the sheriff, 'I'd never dare
    To come before the King;
He'd bind me fast, then round my neck
    He'd loop the hangman's string.'

He searched the streets of Nottingham town,
    Every cranny and nook searched he;
But Robin was home in the greenwood, light
    As a leaf on a linden-tree.

Little John turned to Robin Hood
    And gruffly he did say,
'I did you a good turn for an ill—
    Repay me when you may.
I've brought you safe to the trysting-tree,
    And I'll wish you now good-day.'

'Good giant, you cannot go,' said Robin.
    'No, that shall not be.
I'll serve you true and make you captain
    Of all my men and me.'
'O take me back and I'll stay your man,'
    Said John, and dropped to his knee.

Then every yeoman's heart was glad;
    They passed the bumper round
With wine and ale, and banqueted
    Until the sun went down.

The Fisherman's Catch

When shelduck played with shelduck, quack!
    And fresh and green was the year,
And the lily leaf and the daffodil
    Gave merry April cheer,
Then Robin tired of the good greenwood
    And chasing the fallow-deer.

'Rich is the merchant, richer still
    The harvester of the sea;
And so to Scarborough I will go,
    A fisherman brave to be.'

He said good-bye to his merry men all
    And hastened over the hill
To Scarborough where, by the fishing-fleet,
    The gulls were whistling shrill;
And there he lodged in a widow's cottage
    By the waters, grey and chill.

'O what is your trade,' said the widow, 'and why
    Do you take your lodging here?'
'I'm a poor fisherman,' Robin replied,
    'And out of my luck this year.'

'What is your name, my fine fellow?
    Now tell me true,' said she.
'In the coastal village where I was born
    They call me Simon Lee.'

'Simon—Simon—I like that name,
    And your face a widow can trust;
But the master who hires my ship from me
    Cheats me—he's unjust.

'O Simon, I beg, will you be my man?
    I'll pay you princely wages.
My ship is true, she will not sink,
    However the storm-wind rages.

'Stout are the sails, the decks are pitched,
    The mast is tall and strong.'
'If the ship's as trim as you say,' said he,
    'There's nothing can go wrong.'

They plucked up anchor, away they sailed.
    When full two days had passed,
The others baited their hooks, but bare
    Was the line that Simon cast.

'You brainless lubber!' the master cried.
    'No fisherman you, I swear.
But I'll see no part of our catch shall go
    To a man who shirked his share.'

His shipmates laughed Simon to scorn,
    With many a hoot and jeer,
Till he sighed to be back in Plumpton Park,
    Chasing the fallow-deer.

'He sighs! Simon's in love!' they leered.
    'Lured by the widow's charms!
And if the storm-wind blows, we hope
    'Twill toss him into her arms.'

'This noble fisherman,' they mocked,
    'Will make a noble match.
We'll set his tale to a rollicking tune
    And call it "The Fisherman's Catch".'

They plucked up anchor, away they sailed.
    When full two days had passed,
Simon he spied a ship-of-war,
    Full sail, pursuing them fast.

'Pirates! Frenchmen!' the master cursed.
    'O bitter must be the cost,
For we shall be flung in a Frenchman's jail,
    And all our herring lost!'

Said Simon, 'Master, nothing's yet lost.
    I shall not shirk my share.
Give me my bent bow in my hand—
    Not a Frenchman will I spare.'

'Hold your tongue, you bragging lubber,
    Or I'll make you walk the plank!
There'd be only a bragging lubber lost,
    And none to care if you sank.'

Simon sprang to his feet, his temper
    Flared like an angry spark.
He grabbed his bow, drew the string to his ear—
    Then slipped, and missed his mark.

'O master, tie me straight to the mast!
    With my bent bow firm in my hand,
I'll see that from yonder ship-of-war
    No Frenchman reaches land.'

He drew his arrow to the silver tip,
    With a twang he set it free.
In the twink of an eye a Frenchman fell
    Splash! in the tumbling sea.

Then thick as hail his arrows flew;
    Every Frenchman's life he took.
'Master, untie my ropes,' he cried,
    'And throw your grappling hook!'

They boarded the pirate ship-of-war,
    Swiftly they searched the hold;
And there they found a treasure heaped—
    Twelve thousand pounds in gold.

They sailed her over the tumbling sea,
    They sailed her home with a will,
While the widow waited anxiously
    And the gulls were whistling shrill.

'Half this ship-of-war I'll give
    To my dame and her children small.
The other half,' said Simon, 'I'll share
    Among my shipmates all.

'As for the gold, I'll give it away
    To help the poor and oppressed;
And I'll build a place for the old, where they
    May live in peace and rest.'

Said the widow, 'O Simon, live with me
    And be my husband dear.'
'The lark rings the only wedding bells,'
    Said he, 'that ever I'll hear.' . . .
And back he went to the woods, and stayed
    For more than twenty year.

The Last Arrow

O songless was the misty wood
    And the valley dark with doom,
When Robin Hood and Little John
    Went over yon bank of broom.
'My arrows trail and droop,' said Robin.
    'My heart is sick with gloom.

'I cannot eat, I cannot drink;
    I must hasten now,' he said,
'To the Prioress of Kirkley Hall,
    My cousin, to be bled.'

'Alone you must not go,' said John.
    'Master, that will not do.
Half a hundred bowmen brave
    Shall march along with you.

'For Red Roger is lodging there,—
    He's sure some quarrel to pick.
You may have need of us, master, yet;
    I fear some deadly trick.'

'What, Little John! Are you afraid?
    Then at home your place shall be.'
'If you're angry with me, my master dear,
    You'll never hear more of me.'

'No man in the world shall march with me,
    No man in the world shall ride.
I shall go to Kirkley Hall alone,
    With my bent bow at my side.'

At first his step was quick and strong,
    Then slower it grew and shorter.
Lingering and heavy it was,
    When he came to the black water.

On the crossing-plank there knelt an old woman;
    She cried, her eyes a-gleam,
'Go back! Go back! Or only your ghost
    Glides homeward over this stream.'

Robin heeded her not, but gazed
    Beyond at the forest track.
Then gently over her head he stepped,
    Limped on, and looked not back.

When he came to fair Kirkley Hall
    And knocked three times at the door,
None was so glad as his cousin herself
    To bid him cross her floor.

In league with Red Roger of Doncaster,
    She wished her cousin no good;
Faithless, cruel and false was she,
    And hated Robin Hood.

'Will you please sit down, Cousin Robin,' she said,
    'And drink some ale or beer?'
'No, I will neither eat nor drink
    Until you have bled me here.'

She took him by the lily-white hand
    To a secret room inside,
Then fetched a pair of blood-irons
    In a silken napkin tied.

'Now set a chafing-dish to the fire,'
    She said. 'Roll up your sleeve.'
(How reckless and unwise is he,
    No warning will believe!)

She laid the blood-irons to Robin's arm,
    O, sad it was to see,
As her cruel knife pierced the vein,
    The red blood spilling free!

At first it bled, the thick, thick blood,
    And afterwards the thin.
Then Robin Hood at last was aware
    That treason there was within.

His cousin, the cruel Prioress,
    Locked the door of his room,
And left him there to bleed all night
    Until next day at noon.

He staggered to the shot-window
    And slipped one leg outside.
Red Roger, he was lurking below
    And thrust a spear in his side.

O black was his heart, and red his hair
    As the mane of a chestnut steed!
As his fingers reached for Robin's purse,
    His eyes they smoked with greed.

But Robin, light and nimble of foot,
    Raised his sword in the air
And slashed it on Red Roger's neck,—
    The knuckled bone lay bare.

'Lie there, lie there, Red Roger!' he cried.
    'The dogs your blood shall taste.'
Then he grasped hold of his bugle-horn,
    Hanging low at his waist.

Three times he blew. Said Little John,
    As he sat by the trysting-tree,
'I fear my master is nearly dead,
    He blows so wearily.'

He ran like the wind to Kirkley Hall,
    He knelt at Robin's side.
'Master, a boon, a boon I beg,
    A boon I beg,' he cried.

'What is that boon,' said Robin Hood,
    'Little John, you beg of me?'
'It is to burn fair Kirkley Hall
    And all their nunnery.'

'No, no, you shall not,' said Robin Hood.
   'That boon I'll not agree.
I never hurt woman in all my life,
   Nor man in her company.

'I never hurt maid, or widow, or wife,
   Nor shall I now I die.
But give me my bent bow in my hand,
   And an arrow I'll let fly;
And where it falls you shall dig my grave;
   It's there I long to lie.

'Set my bright sword at my head,
   My arrows at my feet,
And lay my bent bow at my side,
   Which was my music sweet.

'Let me have length and breadth enough,
   And turf from the good greenwood,
That men may say when I am dead,
   "Here lies bold Robin Hood".'

Then with the last of his strength brave Robin
   Drew his bent yew bow,
And the arrow flew over the nunnery wall
   Deep into the glade below.

John gathered him in his giant arms;
   And his heart was sick with gloom,
As under the greenwood tree he dug
   His well loved master's tomb,
And songless was the misty wood
   And the valley dark with doom.